BEGINNINGS

Six Sessions for Spiritual Beginnings

Serendipity House / P.O. Box 1012 / Littleton, CO 80160 / 1-800-525-9563

© 1996 Serendipity House. All Rights Reserved.

96 97 98 99 / **101 series•CHG** / 6 5 4 3 2 1

FOUR THINGS YOU NEED TO KNOW ABOUT

Beginning a Small Group

1. PURPOSE: This course is designed to kick off a small group. The goal is to get acquainted and decide after six weeks if you want to continue as a group. We call this the "birthing period" of a group or 101. Using the analogy of a baseball diamond, the goal is home plate or "bonding." To get to home plate, the group needs to go around three bases: FIRST BASE: History Giving—telling your "story" to one another—your childhood, your journey, your hopes and dreams. SECOND BASE: Affirmation—responding to each other's story with appreciation. THIRD BASE: Need Sharing—going deeper in your story—your present struggles, roadblocks, anxieties, and where you need help from God and the group.

2. AGENDA: There are three parts to every group meeting.

GATHERING / 15 min.
Purpose: To break the ice

BIBLE STUDY / 30 min.
Purpose: To share your spiritual journey

CARING / 45 min.
Purpose: To share prayer requests

3. FEARLESS FOURSOME: If you have more than 7 in your group at any time, call the option play when the time comes for Bible study, and subdivide into groups of 4 for greater participation. (In 4s, everyone will share and you can finish the Bible study in 30 minutes). Then regather the group for the CARING TIME.

GATHERING
All Together

BIBLE STUDY
Groups of 4

CARING
Back Together

4. EMPTY CHAIR: Pull up an empty chair during the **CARING TIME** at the close and ask God to fill this chair each week. Remember, by breaking into groups of 4 for the Bible study time, you can grow numerically without feeling "too big" as a group.

The Group Leader needs an apprentice-in-training at all times so that the apprentice can start a new "cell" when the group size is 12 or more.

SESSION 1

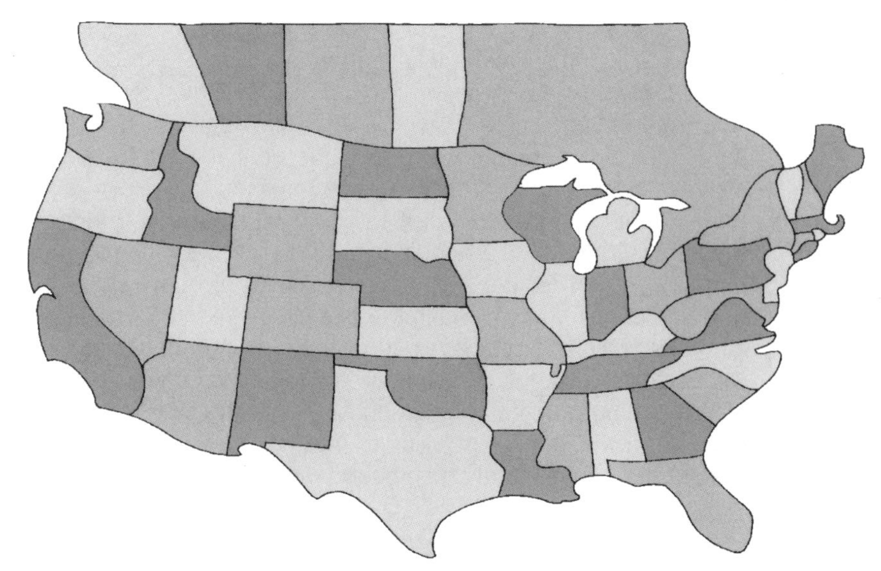

Getting Acquainted

OPEN

GATHERING / 15 Minutes / All Together

Leader: The purpose of the Gathering time is to break the ice and start the sharing on the light side. Keep a record of the time and move on after 15 minutes.

Places In My Life. On the map above, put three dots to indicate these significant places in your journey. Then go around and have each person explain the dots:

- the place where I was born
- the place where I spent most of my life
- the place where I did go or would like to go on a honeymoon

BIBLE STUDY / 30 Minutes / Groups of 4

Leader: Pause at this point and ask the group to focus on page 2 while you explain the purpose and procedures for this six-session course. Then, (1) read the Introduction and (2) encourage the group to subdivide into groups of 4 for the Bible Study discussion—4 at the dining table, 4 at the kitchen table, etc. Ask one person in each foursome to be the Leader and follow the directions. Be sure to regather the entire group for the Caring Time in the last 30-45 minutes of the meeting.

STUDY

Introduction: There are two goals in this course: (1) to give those who are starting off (or starting over) in their Christian life a chance to learn about the basics of a healthy spiritual life, and (2) to experience a small caring group that may want to continue after this course is over as a covenant group.

The Bible study time in this course is designed to meet these two goals. All of the Bible studies are taken from the life of Simon Peter, a typical Christian who went through some growing pains in his rookie years, but ended up being the leader of the church. A two-part questionnaire will help guide your discussion in the Bible study. The questions have multiple-choice options, and there are no right or wrong answers, so you don't have to worry about being "right." If you have more than 7 people in the meeting, we recommend that you divide into groups of 4 for the Bible study discussion. In groups of 4, everyone can participate, and you can finish the questionnaire in 30 minutes. Then, regather all of the groups for the last part of the meeting, the Caring Time, where you will have a chance to talk about the ground rules for your group.

When you get into your group of 4, use the Opening Questions below to decide on the leader of your foursome. Then, have someone read the Scripture passage aloud and proceed with Step 1 in the questionnaire.

Opening Questions (choose one or both)

1. What is your nickname and how did you get it?

2. How many speeding tickets have you received in your lifetime? (The one with the least tickets could be appointed leader for this session).

Bible Story: *The Calling of the First Disciples - Luke 5:1–11*

***5** One day as Jesus was standing by the Lake of Gennesaret, with the people crowding around him and listening to the word of God, [2]he saw at the water's edge two boats, left there by the fishermen, who were washing their nets. [3]He got into one of the boats, the one belonging to Simon, and asked him to put out a little from shore. Then he sat down and taught the people from the boat.*

[4]When he had finished speaking, he said to Simon, "Put out into deep water, and let down the nets for a catch."

[5]Simon answered, "Master, we've worked hard all night and haven't caught anything. But because you say so, I will let down the nets."

[6]When they had done so, they caught such a large number of fish that their nets began to break. [7]So they signaled their partners in the other boat to come and help them, and they came and filled both boats so full that they began to sink.

[8]When Simon Peter saw this, he fell at Jesus' knees and said, "Go away from me, Lord; I am a sinful man!" [9]For he and all his companions were astonished at the catch of fish they had taken, [10]and so were James and John, the sons of Zebedee, Simon's partners.

Then Jesus said to Simon, "Don't be afraid; from now on you will catch men." [11]So they pulled their boats up on shore, left everything and followed him.

Looking Into the Story. The following two-part questionnaire is designed for easy sharing—with multiple-choice options to choose from. Ask one person to answer question #1 and explain why. The next person takes question #2, etc. There are no right or wrong answers, so feel free to share.

1. If you can, imagine Peter sitting there in his boat. What was he thinking about while Jesus was teaching the crowd?
   - ❑ Oh no—another visiting preacher.
   - ❑ Say what?
   - ❑ I wish he would finish so I can have my boat back.
   - ❑ Hey, this guy could give me a few lessons.
   - ❑ I've always wanted to give my life to something. I wonder if this is it.

2. When Jesus invited him to go fishing in the "deep water," what do you think Peter said to himself?
   - ❑ This guy must not know much about fishing. You don't fish with "nets" in deep water!
   - ❑ I've been fishing all night and I know there are no fish out there.
   - ❑ Hey, I just got my nets dry and folded up. I don't want to get them wet.
   - ❑ Stick to your preaching ... and I'll stick to fishing.

3. When they "caught a large number" of fish, what was Simon Peter saying to himself now?
   - ❑ This is my lucky day!
   - ❑ I can hardly wait to tell my buddies about this haul!
   - ❑ Who is this guy Jesus?
   - ❑ I feel awful.
   - ❑ I wish I could stay with Jesus forever.

4. On the day that Peter parked his boat and joined Jesus, what chances would you give this guy of becoming the rookie of the year and going on to become the leader of the church?
   - ❑ a whole lot—he showed lots of promise
   - ❑ a little—he was a diamond in the rough
   - ❑ very little
   - ❑ not a chance

STEP 2

My Own Story: In this step, go around on question #1 and ask everyone to share their answer. Then, go around again on question #2, etc. Remember to save the last 30 to 45 minutes in this meeting to regather for the Caring Time.

1. When was the first time you recall feeling the tug of Jesus on your heart?
   - ❑ when I was very young
   - ❑ when there was a crisis in my life
   - ❑ when I was away on a retreat
   - ❑ just recently
   - ❑ I don't know that I have.
   - ❑ other:____________________

2. How are you and Jesus getting along now?
   - ❑ We're not talking.
   - ❑ We're dating a little.
   - ❑ We're going steady.
   - ❑ We're doing great.
   - ❑ We broke up.
   - ❑ Jesus who?
   - ❑ other:__________________

3. If Jesus invited you to push out into "deep water," what would you say?
   - ❑ I'm afraid of deep water.
   - ❑ I'm not ready for deep water.
   - ❑ Fine, as long as I can wear a life jacket.
   - ❑ Give me a minute.
   - ❑ Great, let's go.
   - ❑ other:________________________

4. What caused you to come to this small group?
   - ❑ my mother made me
   - ❑ curiosity
   - ❑ a suspicion that I needed to work on my spiritual life
   - ❑ a hunger to know God better
   - ❑ a desire to belong to a group that can help each other in their spiritual growth
   - ❑ other:________________________

5. How do you feel about talking over your spiritual struggles with a group of fellow strugglers?
   - ❑ fine, if I know them
   - ❑ okay, if I can trust them
   - ❑ I get uptight when I am asked to share anything personal.
   - ❑ I got hurt once in a group situation.
   - ❑ great, if nobody tries to preach

6. If you are going to give yourself to this group for all six sessions, what do you want understood from the beginning?
   - ❑ This is a group for strugglers, not saints.
   - ❑ Everyone participates, no spectators.
   - ❑ I can say "I pass" at any time.
   - ❑ Bible knowledge is not a prerequisite.
   - ❑ We will respect each other—and each other's opinions.

CARING TIME / 45 Minutes / All Together

Leader: Bring all of the groups back together for a time of caring. In this first session, you need to set the ground rules and goals for your group. After this, spend the remaining time in prayer requests and prayer.

Introduction: Now is the time to decide what you want to get out of this course. For yourself. Your group. And to agree on the ground rules for your group. Follow these steps.

SHARING

Step One: Expectations. Give everyone a chance to share two things that you would like to get out of this course and this group, starting with the list below:

- ❑ a closer walk with God
- ❑ to understand what a personal faith in Christ means

- ❑ to be in a group where I can deal with the struggles I have as a Christian
- ❑ to learn about my church
- ❑ to discover what God wants me to do with my life
- ❑ to get to know some Christians in this church
- ❑ to learn about the Bible
- ❑ to learn how to pray
- ❑ to have fun
- ❑ to rethink my lifestyle, now that I have committed my life to Christ
- ❑ to find my niche in the church
- ❑ other:____

Step Two: Ground Rules. What are some ground rules that you would like to set for this group? See if you can agree on two or three.

- ❑ ATTENDANCE: Group members will give priority to the group meetings for six weeks or sessions.
- ❑ STUPID QUESTIONS: This is a beginner's group for beginning Christians. "Dumb" questions are encouraged.
- ❑ MISSION: This group will be "open" to anyone who is seeking or who is starting over in the Christian life ... and it will be the mission of this group to invite new people to every session.
- ❑ ACCOUNTABILITY: This group will be a support group. Prayer requests will be shared at the end of every session and group members will be encouraged to call each other to ask, "How's it going?"
- ❑ CONFIDENTIALITY: Anything said in the group is kept in confidence.
- ❑ COVENANT: At the end of this course, the group will evaluate the experience and decide if they wish to continue as a covenant group.

PRAYER

Step Three: Prayer Requests. At the close of every session, give the group a chance to share their prayer concerns. Here is a good question to ask everyone to answer:

"How can we help you in prayer this week?"

Step Four: Prayer. Here is a very simple form of prayer. Go around and let everyone finish the sentence:

"Hello God, this is ... (first name), I want to thank you for ..."

If you would like to say your prayer in silence, say the word "Amen" when you have finished your prayer so that the next person will know when to start.

P.S. Pass around your books and have everyone put their names in the GROUP DIRECTORY inside the front cover.

*Let me guess .... that **Jesus** fellow again ...*

When Did Jesus Become More Than a Name?

OPEN

GATHERING / 15 Minutes / All Together

Leader: Welcome newcomers and add their names to the Directory inside the front cover. The goal for this session is to let everyone share their spiritual background. The following ice-breaker is designed to start your meeting. Call time after 15 minutes and move on.

Down Memory Lane. Celebrate the childhood memories of the way you were. Choose one or more of the topics listed below and answer the question related to it. If time allows, do another round.

HOME SWEET HOME—What do you remember about your childhood home?

TELEVISION—What was your favorite TV program?

OLD SCHOOL HOUSE—What were your best and worst subjects in school?

LIBRARY—What did you like to read (and where)?

TELEPHONE—How much time did you spend on the phone each day?

MOVIES—Who was your favorite movie star?

CASH FLOW—What did you do for spending money?

SPORTS—What was your favorite sport or team?

GRANDPA'S HOUSE—Where did your grandparents live? When did you visit them?

POLICE—Did you ever get in trouble with the law?

WEEKENDS—What was the thing to do on Saturday night?

BIBLE STUDY / 30 Minutes / Groups of 4

Leader: Pause at this point for a quick review of page 2. If you have more than 7 in your group, divide into subgroups—but not the same foursome as last week. Ask one person in each group to be the Leader and complete the Bible study in 30 minutes. Then regather for the Caring Time.

OPEN

Introduction: Remember the two goals in this course: (1) to find out what the Christian life is all about, and (2) to experience a Christian small group that supports one another in the journey.

In the last session, you met Simon Peter in the Bible story. In this session, you will study the day Jesus asked Simon the crucial question about his personal faith. In the process, you will have a chance to share your own response to this crucial question.

If you have more than 7 in your group, we suggest that you divide into groups of 4 for this discussion—4 at the dining table, 4 at the kitchen table, etc. Then, you can come back together at the end of the Bible study for the Caring Time. Start off with the Opening Questions below. Then have someone read the Scripture passage and the instructions for Step 1 in the questionnaire.

Opening Questions: (choose one or two of the following)

1. In your group, who cannot pass a garage sale without stopping?

2. In your group, who has overdrawn their bank account recently?

3. In your group, who screams and hollers at referees?

Bible Story: ***Peter's Confession of Christ - Luke 9:18–25***

[18]Once when Jesus was praying in private and his disciples were with him, he asked them, "Who do the crowds say I am?"

[19]They replied, "Some say John the Baptist; others say Elijah; and still others, that one of the prophets of long ago has come back to life."

[20]"But what about you?" he asked. "Who do you say I am?"

Peter answered, "The Christ of God."

[21]Jesus strictly warned them not to tell this to anyone. [22]And he said, "The Son of Man must suffer many things and be rejected by the elders, chief priests and teachers of the law, and he must be killed and on the third day be raised to life."

[23]Then he said to them all: "If anyone would come after me, he must deny himself and take up his cross daily and follow me. [24]For whoever wants to save his life will lose it, but whoever loses his life for me will save it. [25]What good is it for a man to gain the whole world, and yet lose or forfeit his very self?

Looking Into the Story: The following two-part questionnaire is designed for easy sharing—with multiple-choice options to choose from. Ask one person to answer question #1 and explain why. The next person takes question #2, etc. There are no right or wrong answers, so feel free to share.

1. Why do you think Jesus asked his disciples who people said he was?
   - ❑ He was concerned about what people thought of him.
   - ❑ He was searching himself for who he was.
   - ❑ He wanted to find out how well he was revealing himself.
   - ❑ He wanted the disciples to think about who *they* thought he was.

2. If the local TV reporter interviewed the average person in your community with the same question Jesus asked—"Who do the crowds say I am"—what would they say?
   - ❑ a great teacher
   - ❑ a swear word
   - ❑ the Son of God
   - ❑ a lot of rubbish
   - ❑ stained glass windows
   - ❑ someone you pray to
   - ❑ a nice guy
   - ❑ preacher against fun
   - ❑ the founder of the Christian religion
   - ❑ someone who died long ago on a cross
   - ❑ the Messiah—the Savior of the world
   - ❑ holy man (more spiritual than real)

3. Why do you think the crowds in Jesus' day would mistake Jesus for John the Baptist, Elijah or one of the prophets of long ago who has come back to life?
   - ❑ Because he acted weird.
   - ❑ He ran around with common people.
   - ❑ He spoke out on political issues.
   - ❑ He ate with sinners.
   - ❑ He offered hope to people who had no hope.
   - ❑ He didn't act religious.

4. How do you think Peter came up with the right answer—"You are the Christ, God's Messiah"?
   - ❑ His old mentor John the Baptist told him.
   - ❑ He had been studying Old Testament prophecy himself.
   - ❑ He had seen how Jesus loved and healed people.
   - ❑ It was a revelation from God.

5. "If anyone would come after me, he must deny himself and take up his cross daily and follow me." What is Jesus saying?
   - ❑ Following Jesus is no rose garden.
   - ❑ If you've got reservations, now is the time to get out.
   - ❑ It's gonna cost you everything.
   - ❑ Shape up or ship out.

My Own Story: In this step, go around on question #1 and ask everyone to share their answer. Then, go around again on question #2, etc. through the questions. Be sure to save the last 30 minutes at the close for the Caring Time.

1. When you compare your Christian life to what Jesus calls you to do—to deny yourself and take up your cross daily—how do you feel?
   - ❏ like starting over
   - ❏ like crawling under the rug
   - ❏ like going for it
   - ❏ like running away
   - ❏ like yawning

2. What would it mean for you to "deny" yourself?
   - ❏ to stop focusing on all my problems, and think more about others
   - ❏ to never do anything for myself
   - ❏ to go less to the mall or golf course and more to visit the rest homes
   - ❏ to put Christ's desires/will above my own

3. What would it mean for you to "gain the whole world, and yet lose or forfeit your very self"?
   - ❏ gain the approval of significant people, but give up what I stand for
   - ❏ gain the world's approval, but lose Christ's approval
   - ❏ gain in career or possessions, but lose what's most important in life

4. What do you need to do to take the next step in your spiritual life?
   - ❏ correct some of my misconceptions of who Jesus is
   - ❏ do remedial work on the basics—prayer, Bible reading, etc.
   - ❏ confess my faith publicly
   - ❏ find my spiritual potential

CARING TIME / 45 Minutes / All Together

Leader: Call all of the groups back together for a time of caring. Start off by turning to the Caring Time in the last session, especially the EXPECTATIONS and GOALS you set as a group.

Step One: Weekly Report. Go around your group and let everyone explain their spiritual life this past week by choosing a number from 1 to 10—1 being TERRIBLE and 10 being GREAT. Finish the sentence, *"This past week has been a ..."* and explain. For instance, *"This past week has been a 7 ... Most of the time, I really felt God's presence ... but there were a few times when I felt like someone had cut the phone line ..."*

SHARING

Step Two. Take some time to share any personal prayer requests by answering the question:

"How can we help you in prayer this week?"

PRAYER

Step Three. Close with a short time of prayer, remembering the requests that have been shared. If you would like to say your prayer in silence, say the word "Amen" when you have finished your prayer so that the next person will know when to start.

SESSION

3

Howdy! What did I miss?

How's It Going in Your Life?

OPEN

GATHERING / 15 Minutes / All Together

Leader: Welcome any newcomers and add their names to the Directory. The purpose of this session is to share your spiritual life right now—"How's it going?" The fun ice-breaker is designed to prepare you for this deeper sharing.

Dream Wheels. If you could choose two cars for your life—one for work and another for play—what would you choose? Go around and let everyone explain their choices.

SPORTS CAR: Fire-red Corvette, with cellular telephone

ALL-TERRAIN VEHICLE: Camouflage-green Hummer

CLASSIC CAR: Rebuilt '65 Ford Mustang convertible

4-WHEEL: Heavy-duty Jeep Grand Cherokee

TOWN CAR: Lincoln Continental with refreshment bar

COMIC CAR: 1974 Volkswagen with Rolls Royce front

PICK UP: Dodge Ram 4 x 4 with roll bar

ANTIQUE CAR: 1929 Model A Ford with rumble seat

CIRCUS CAR: Ringling Brothers and Barnum & Bailey variety

RACING CAR: Turbo-charged Porsche with air foils and spoilers

'50s CAR: Red T-Bird with fur steering wheel and leopard upholstery

BIBLE STUDY / 30 Minutes / Groups of 4

Leader: If you have more than 7 in this session, we recommend groups of 4—but not the same foursomes as last week. Ask one person in each foursome to be the Leader and complete the Bible study in 30 minutes. Then regather for the Caring Time.

STUDY

Introduction: Welcome to the real world in the Christian life: the world of super highs and super lows ... rainy days ... and balmy, boring days. Days when your prayers go no higher than the ceiling ... and you feel as low as a duck's instep. Days of disappointment and failure. In the Bible study for this session, you are going to see one of those days in action.

The Bible story is about a vacation that Jesus took with his disciples—a vacation that turned into a disaster when a "storm" blew up. Start off with the Opening Question. Then, have someone read out loud the Bible story.

If there are more than 7 in your group, be sure to divide into groups of 4 (not the same 4s as last week) and ask one person in the group to be the leader. Then, be ready to come back together for the last 30-45 minutes for the Caring Time.

Opening Question:

Which three things are guaranteed to ruin a vacation for you?

- ❑ seven straight days of rain
- ❑ phone calls from the office
- ❑ running into friends from home
- ☑ losing luggage
- ❑ mosquitoes/ants
- ❑ unfinished business at work
- ☑ losing your wallet
- ☑ car trouble
- ❑ losing your way
- ❑ having relatives along
- ❑ no flush toilets
- ❑ standing in long lines

Bible Story: ***Jesus Calms the Storm - Mark 4:35–41***

[35]That day when evening came, he said to his disciples, "Let us go over to the other side." [36]Leaving the crowd behind, they took him along, just as he was, in the boat. There were also other boats with him. [37]A furious squall came up, and the waves broke over the boat, so that it was nearly swamped. [38]Jesus was in the stern, sleeping on a cushion. The disciples woke him and said to him, "Teacher, don't you care if we drown?"

[39]He got up, rebuked the wind and said to the waves, "Quiet! Be still!" Then the wind died down and it was completely calm.

[40]He said to his disciples, "Why are you so afraid? Do you still have no faith?"

[41]They were terrified and asked each other, "Who is this? Even the wind and the waves obey him!"

STEP 1 **Looking Into the Story:** The following two-part questionnaire is designed for easy sharing—with multiple-choice options to choose from. Ask one person to answer question #1 and explain why. The next person takes question #2, etc. There are no right or wrong answers, so feel free to share.

1. If you had been one of the disciples when the boat was about to sink, what would you have done?
   - ❑ jumped overboard
   - ❑ started bailing water
   - ❑ woken up Jesus
   - ❑ screamed for help
   - ❑ taken command

2. Why do you think the disciples awakened Jesus?
   - ❑ They were afraid for his life.
   - ❑ They were afraid for their own lives.
   - ❑ They wanted all the help they could get to bail.
   - ❑ They wanted Jesus to perform another miracle.
   - ❑ They were mad that Jesus was sleeping through their crisis.

3. What was the tone in Jesus' voice when he asked, "Why are you so afraid? Do you still have no faith?"
   - ❑ scolding—"You guys are a bunch of wimps."
   - ❑ disappointment—"Don't you know I am not going to let you down?"
   - ❑ compassion—"I know you are scared."
   - ❑ resentment—"Why did you wake me up?"

4. Why did Jesus allow a storm to come up in the first place?
   - ❑ He didn't—storms come up naturally.
   - ❑ He was asleep at the switch.
   - ❑ He wanted to test them.
   - ❑ He wanted to help them when they asked.
   - ❑ He wanted to stretch their faith.

STEP 2 **My Own Story:** In this step, go around on question #1 and ask everyone to share their answer. Then, go around again on question #2, etc. Remember to save the last 30 to 45 minutes in this meeting to regather for the Caring Time.

1. What do you do when "storms" come up in your life?
   - 2 ❑ turn to a person I can trust
   - ❑ act like nothing is wrong
   - 1 ❑ withdraw into myself
   - ❑ panic
   - 4 ❑ turn to God
   - 3 ❑ take charge of things
   - ❑ get very touchy and irritable

2. How would you compare your life right now to the storm in this story?
   - ❑ smooth sailing—enjoying the ride
   - ❑ choppy water—a few ripples
   - ❑ furious squall—sinking fast
   - ❑ storm over—cleaning up the mess

insecurity

3. What brings on the storms in your life?
   - ❑ financial difficulties
   - ❑ insecurity: job/finances
   - ❑ tragedy: sickness/death
   - ☑ hassles with relationships
   - ❑ disappointment
   - ❑ overwhelming demands

4. "Quiet! Be Still!" If Jesus were to speak these words to you today, what would they mean?
   - ❑ settle down
   - ❑ relax and let God handle this
   - ☑ turn control of your life over to God
   - ❑ hang in there
   - ❑ shut up and listen

CARING TIME / 45 Minutes / All Together

Leader: Bring the groups of 4 back together and take a quick check on how everyone is feeling about this group. Step One is designed to help you in this. Then move on to prayer requests and prayer.

Step One: Where Are You Sitting? Imagine that your group is a team in the stadium, playing the game. How do you feel about the group so far? Where are you in relation to the action? Here are some options. Finish the sentence: "In this group up to now, I have been sitting ..."

- ❑ in the grandstands: just looking on, not really involved
- ❑ on the bench: on the team, but not playing
- ❑ on injured reserves: in the locker room, checking out some bruises
- ☑ out on the field, playing defense: pretty conservative
- ❑ out on the field, playing offense: giving it all I've got

SHARING

Step Two: If you have time, give everyone a chance to answer the question below:

"How can we help you in prayer this week?"

PRAYER

Step Three: Go around and pray for the person on your right by finishing this sentence:

"Hello, God, I want to thank you for ... (first name) ..."

If you would like to say your prayer in silence, say the word "Amen" when you have finished your prayer so that the next person will know when to start.

... O Merciful Lord, bless our beloved brother Thomas ... the old coot ...

How Can We Help You in Prayer?

OPEN

GATHERING / 15 Minutes / All Together

Leader: Welcome newcomers and add their names to the Directory inside the front cover. This is going to be a heavy session. Start the meeting on the light side with this ice-breaker.

Broadway Show. In every group, there comes a time when you need to say, "Thanks for sharing." This is what this session is all about. In the ice-breaker, you will have a chance to say this in a fun way. And in the Caring Time at the close, you will have a chance to say this in a serious way.

Imagine for a moment that your group has been chosen to produce a Broadway Show, and you had to choose people from your group for all of the jobs for this production. Have someone read out loud the job description for the first job below—PRODUCER. Then, let everyone in your group call out the name of the person in your group who would best fit this job. (You don't have to agree.) Then read the job description for the next job and let everyone call out the name of the best person for this job, etc.

You only have 15 minutes for this assignment, so move fast.

PRODUCER: Typical Hollywood business tycoon, extravagant, big-budget, big-production magnate in the Steven Spielberg style.

DIRECTOR: Creative, imaginative brains behind the scene; perfectionist, big-spender, unpredictable genius.

HEROINE: Beautiful, captivating, seductive, everybody's heart throb; defenseless when men are around, but nobody's fool.

HERO: Tough, macho, champion of the underdog, knight in shining armor; Mr. Clutch in the John Wayne mold, always gets his man.

COMEDIAN: Childlike, happy-go-lucky, outrageously funny, covers up a brilliant interior with a carefully tailored "clown" exterior.

CHARACTER PERSON: One-of-a-kind eccentric, rugged individualist, outrageously different, colorful, adds spice to any surrounding.

FALL GUY: Studied, nonchalant character, who wins the hearts of everyone by being the "foil" of the heavy characters.

TECHNICAL DIRECTOR: The genius for "sound and lights," complete with beard, tennis shoes, "off the wall" T-shirt and jogging shorts.

COMPOSER OF LYRICS: Communicates in music what everybody understands, heavy into feelings, moods, outbursts of energy.

PUBLICITY AGENT: Mafia leader turned Madison Avenue executive, knows all the angles, good at one-liners, a flair for "hot" news.

VILLAIN: The "bad guy" who really is the heavy for the plot, forces others to think, challenges traditional values; out to destroy "cliches," shallow morality, and plastic conformity.

AUTHOR: Shy, aloof, eccentric person, very much in touch with feelings, sensitive to people, puts into words what others only feel.

BIBLE STUDY / 30 Minutes / All Together

Leader: If you have more than 7 in your group, be sure to subdivide into groups of 4. Ask one in each group to be the Leader and to stick to the agenda.

STUDY

Introduction: In the first three sessions, you have seen Simon Peter on the day he met Jesus Christ, the day he confessed Jesus was the Son of God, and the day that he went through a storm with Jesus. In this session, you will see Simon Peter on the day he "hit bottom" spiritually.

The story begins on the last night that Jesus spent with his disciples. At the Passover meal (a Jewish custom), Jesus explains the new meaning of the "bread and wine." (This is the reason Christians celebrate the "Last Supper" with new meaning.) Then, Jesus explains that one of the disciples will betray him. Immediately, all of the disciples get defensive, especially Simon Peter. Listen to the story. Then, move into groups of 4 and discuss the questionnaire.

Opening Questions (choose one or both)

1. Where do you keep your trophies (or keepsakes) that have special value?
- ❑ in a scrapbook
- ❑ in a drawer
- ❑ in Mom's keeping
- ❑ pinned on the wall
- ❑ in a safe deposit box
- ❑ I don't have any.

2. What is one of your youthful failures—where you felt like you let down your friends, family and the world?
   - ❑ dropping the game-winning pass in high school
   - ❑ flunking out of college
   - ❑ getting drunk and disappointing my mother
   - ❑ other:______________________

STUDY

Bible Story: *The Last Supper - Luke 22:31–34,60–62*

[31]"Simon, Simon, Satan has asked to sift you as wheat. [32]But I have prayed for you, Simon, that your faith may not fail. And when you have turned back, strengthen your brothers."

[33]But he [Simon Peter] replied, "Lord, I am ready to go with you to prison and to death."

[34]Jesus answered, "I tell you, Peter, before the rooster crows today, you will deny three times that you know me."

(And later that night, when Simon Peter was recognized as one of Jesus' followers, he proceeded to deny Jesus three times.)

Peter Disowns Jesus

[60]Peter replied, "Man, I don't know what you're talking about!" Just as he was speaking, the rooster crowed. [61]The Lord turned and looked straight at Peter. Then Peter remembered the word the Lord had spoken to him: "Before the rooster crows today, you will disown me three times." [62]And he went outside and wept bitterly.

STEP 1

Looking Into the Story. The following two-part questionnaire is designed for easy sharing—with multiple-choice options to choose from. Ask one person to answer question #1 and explain why. The next person takes question #2, etc. There are no right or wrong answers, so feel free to share.

1. What made Simon Peter do what he did?
   - ❑ spiritual immaturity
   - ❑ momentary insanity
   - ❑ his personality
   - ❑ fear for his life
   - ❑ other:____________

2. If you could put in a good word for Peter, what would you say?
   - ❑ He meant well.
   - ❑ He was only human
   - ❑ He followed Jesus to his trial which is more than the other disciples did.
   - ❑ He came back to Christ in the end—that's the important thing.

3. If you had been Peter's roommate and you knew this about Peter, could you honestly recommend him as a leader in the future church?
   - ❑ No way, he might do it again.
   - ❑ Well, I would put him on probation.
   - ❑ Sure, forgiveness is what the church is all about.
   - ❑ Absolutely, this defeat made him a better person.

4. On a scale from 1 to 10, how would you rank Peter on these character traits?

ON SPIRITUAL DESIRE
1 2 3 4 5 6 7 8 9 10

ON SPIRITUAL CONSISTENCY
1 2 3 4 5 6 7 8 9 10

ON GOING THE DISTANCE
1 2 3 4 5 6 7 8 9 10

STEP 2

My Own Story: In this step, go around on question #1 and ask everyone to share their answer. Then, go around again on question #2, etc. Remember to save the last 30 to 45 minutes in this meeting to regather for the Caring Time.

1. On a scale from 1 to 10, how would you rank yourself on these character traits?

On spiritual desire	1	2	3	4	5	6	7	8	9	10
On spiritual consistency	1	2	3	4	5	6	7	8	9	10
On going the distance	1	2	3	4	5	6	7	8	9	10

2. How do you usually react when you blow it?
   - ❑ kick myself for days
   - ❑ become afraid to try again
   - ❑ pretend that everything is okay
   - ❑ try to be extra good for awhile
   - ❑ admit it and get on with life
   - ❑ talk to God about it

3. What is the closest you have come to throwing out your personal faith?
   - ❑ when my parents split up
   - ❑ when I went off to college
   - ❑ when I went through a personal crisis
   - ❑ when I was away from all of my Christian friends
   - ❑ other:____________________

4. What got you started on the road to recovery?
   - ❑ some caring people
   - ❑ taking some time off to be alone
   - ❑ screaming at God
   - ❑ other:____________________
   - ❑ studying the Bible
   - ❑ crying a lot
   - ❑ getting on with life

5. What have you found helpful in dealing with failure?
   - ❑ watch reruns all night
   - ❑ take some time off
   - ❑ spend time with God
   - ❑ talk it over with a friend
   - ❑ do penance
   - ❑ forget about it/get on with life

CARING TIME / 45 Minutes / All Together

Leader: This is a very pivotal session. When someone steps out and shares their story, it is really important for the group to affirm them. Step One is designed for this. Then move into prayer requests and prayer in Step Two.

AFFIRMATION

Step One: At the beginning of this session, you had a chance to observe the good qualities in each other in a fun way—with jobs in a Broadway Show.

Now, we want you to do the same thing in a more serious way. Ask one person in your group to sit quietly while the others think of the thing that you appreciate most about this person ... or the gift that this person has made to your group in their sharing.

Then, go around and let everyone say what came to mind. For instance, one person might say to Mary,

"Mary, I have appreciated the things you have shared about your spiritual journey ...

or

... the gift that you gave to me in sharing your story was the way you deal with the pain that you have gone through ..."

When you have finished with the first person, ask another person to sit quietly while the others affirm this person, etc ... around the group.

Jesus called Simon Peter a "rock" while he was just a spiritual lump of play dough. Sometimes, others can see in us what we cannot see in ourselves.

Now, ask one person to sit quietly while the others finish one of these two sentences ... with affirmation.

"The thing I appreciate about you is ..."

or

"The gift that you gave to me in sharing your story was ..."

PRAYER

Step Two: Take time to let everyone answer this question and close in prayer.

"How can we help you in prayer this week?"

Hold it! What's this fine print?

What Is God Asking You to Do?

OPEN

GATHERING / 15 Minutes / All Together

Leader: Because this session is more serious, the ice-breaker is too. Give everyone a few seconds to think about their answer. Then share your responses.

How Is It With Your Soul? John Wesley, the founder of the Methodist Church, asked his "class meetings" to check in each week at their small group meeting with this question: "How is it with your soul?"

To answer this question, choose one of these four allegories to explain the past week in your life:

WEATHER: For example: "This week has been mostly cloudy, with some thunderstorms at mid-week. Right now, the weather is a little brighter ..."

MUSIC: For example: "This past week has been like heavy rock music—almost too loud. The sound seems to reverberate off the walls."

COLOR: For example: "This week has been mostly fall colors—deep orange, flaming red, and pumpkin."

SEASON OF THE YEAR: For example: "The season this past week has been like spring-time. New signs of life are beginning to appear on the barren trees, and a few shoots of winter wheat are breaking through the frozen ground."

BIBLE STUDY / 30 Minutes / Groups of 4

Leader: If there are more than 7, subdivide into groups of 4 and ask one in each foursome to be the Leader.

STUDY

Introduction: You have looked at four days in Simon Peter's life: (1) the day he met Jesus, (2) the day he confessed Jesus to be the Son of God, (3) the day he went through a storm with Jesus, and (4) the day he denied Jesus.

In this session, you are going to meet Peter in another impulsive situation—when he tried to walk on water. In the process, you will have a chance to talk about some of your own "water-walking experiences." Be sure to save the last 30-45 minutes at the close for the Caring Time. Now, subdivide into groups of 4 and listen to the Bible story.

Opening Questions (choose one or both)

1. When you were growing up, what was the closest you came to being a daredevil?
   - ❑ motorcycle stunts
   - ❑ mountain climbing
   - ❑ drag racing
   - ❑ surfing
   - ❑ other:__________________

2. What is the closest you come right now to being a daredevil?
   - ❑ getting out of bed
   - ❑ driving on the expressway
   - ❑ investing in the stock market
   - ❑ watching TV
   - ❑ hang gliding
   - ❑ other:__________________

Bible Story: *Jesus Walks on the Water - Matthew 14:22–33*

22Immediately Jesus made the disciples get into the boat and go on ahead of him to the other side, while he dismissed the crowd. 23After he had dismissed them, he went up on a mountainside by himself to pray. When evening came, he was there alone, 24but the boat was already a considerable distance from land, buffeted by the waves because the wind was against it.

25During the fourth watch of the night Jesus went out to them, walking on the lake. 26When the disciples saw him walking on the lake, they were terrified. "It's a ghost," they said, and cried out in fear.

27But Jesus immediately said to them: "Take courage! It is I. Don't be afraid."

28"Lord, if it's you," Peter replied, "tell me to come to you on the water."

29"Come," he said.

Then Peter got down out of the boat, walked on the water and came toward Jesus. 30But when he saw the wind, he was afraid and, beginning to sink, cried out, "Lord, save me!"

31Immediately Jesus reached out his hand and caught him. "You of little faith," he said, "why did you doubt?"

32And when they climbed into the boat, the wind died down. 33Then those who were in the boat worshiped him, saying, "Truly you are the Son of God."

STEP 1

Looking Into the Story. The following two-part questionnaire is designed for easy sharing—with multiple-choice options to choose from. Ask one person to answer question #1 and explain why. The next person takes question #2, etc. There are no right or wrong answers, so feel free to share.

1. If you had been in the boat with the disciples when they saw someone walking on the water, what would you have said?
- ❏ "I think I ate too many anchovies."
- ❏ "Where's Jesus!"
- ❏ "I'm seeing things."
- ❏ "Let me out of here!"
- ❏ I would have said absolutely nothing.

2. What was Jesus saying when he cried out: "Take courage! It is I. Don't be afraid"?
- ❏ Get yourself together.
- ❏ Don't panic.
- ❏ Relax ... believe in me.
- ❏ Why are you surprised? ... You saw me feed 5,000 people today.

3. When Peter replied, "If it's you, tell me to come to you on the water," what was he asking for?
- ❏ the same power Jesus had
- ❏ a little proof
- ❏ an invitation to risk
- ❏ a chance to show off
- ❏ to get to Jesus
- ❏ an opportunity to test his own faith

4. What made Peter sink?
- ❏ His sandals got waterlogged.
- ❏ He lost confidence in himself.
- ❏ His focus shifted from Jesus to his circumstances.
- ❏ His fear was greater than his faith.
- ❏ He realized how foolish he had been to step out of the boat.

5. What was the tone in Jesus' voice when he said, "You of little faith ... why did you doubt?"
- ❏ disappointment: When are you ever going to learn?
- ❏ concern: What happened? You almost drowned.
- ❏ anguish: Oh, Peter! I know what you are going through.
- ❏ anger: Don't ever do that again.

6. If Jesus knew Peter was going to sink, why did he invite him to "come"?
- ❏ to teach him a lesson
- ❏ to encourage him to take risks
- ❏ to test his faith
- ❏ to let him fail

STEP 2

My Own Story: In this step, go around on question #1 and ask everyone to share their answer. Then, go around again on question #2, etc. Remember to save the last 30 to 45 minutes for the Caring Time.

1. How are you at "stepping out of the boat" and taking risks?
   - ❑ just plain scared
   - ❑ daring
   - ❑ I'll try anything once.
   - ❑ I'm good at going second.
   - ❑ cautious—I put my big toe in first.

2. If God called you on the phone today and invited you to join him in a real adventure, what would you do?
   - ❑ wonder what he was up to
   - ❑ ask who else was coming
   - ❑ go reluctantly
   - ❑ check it out first
   - ❑ jump at the chance

3. Where have you made the most progress in your spiritual life?
   - ❑ personal discipline
   - ❑ moral choices
   - ❑ spiritual development
   - ❑ mental attitude
   - ❑ self-acceptance
   - ❑ Bible understanding
   - ❑ willingness to open up and share
   - ❑ concern for others
   - ❑ attitude about work
   - ❑ family relationships

4. What is the next big challenge you need to face?
   - ❑ settling down
   - ❑ learning how to focus my energy
   - ❑ relationships with the opposite sex
   - ❑ making moral decisions
   - ❑ developing my self-confidence
   - ❑ dealing with relationships at home
   - ❑ building a deeper relationship with God

5. Before you can do this, what is standing in the way?
   - ❑ fear of failure
   - ❑ my negative thoughts
   - ❑ inconsistency
   - ❑ intellectual doubts
   - ❑ fear of standing alone
   - ❑ bad family relationships
   - ❑ sense of inadequacy
   - ❑ impulse to rush into things before counting the cost

6. If God challenged you right now about this thing, what would he likely do?
   - ❑ chew me out
   - ❑ be patient with me
   - ❑ work with me extra hours
   - ❑ give me a good kick in the pants
   - ❑ tell me to go home and rest
   - ❑ put his arm around me and tell me that he is proud of me

CARING TIME / 45 Minutes / All Together

Leader: Give everyone time to choose two verses in Step One in silence before sharing. You may want to challenge everyone to write the verse(s) on a card and put it on their dashboard to memorize before next week.

SHARING

Step One: Pick a Promise to Feast On. If you could have two promises—one as a "life verse" and another for right now—which would you choose? Read over the list below and check two, and then share them with the group.

... being confident of this, that he who began a good work in you will carry it on to completion until the day of Christ Jesus. Philippians 1:6

"Come to me, all you who are weary and burdened, and I will give you rest. Take my yoke upon you and learn from me, for I am gentle and humble in heart, and you will find rest for your souls. For my yoke is easy and my burden is light." Matthew 11:28-30

Do not be anxious about anything, but in everything, by prayer and petition, with thanksgiving, present your requests to God. And the peace of God, which transcends all understanding, will guard your hearts and your minds in Christ Jesus. Philippians 4:6-7

"Here I am! I stand at the door and knock. If anyone hears my voice and opens the door, I will come in and eat with him, and he with me." Revelation 3:20

And God is able to make all grace abound to you, so that in all things at all times, having all that you need, you will abound in every good work. 2 Corinthians 9:8

I can do everything through him who gives me strength. Philippians 4:13

Therefore, if anyone is in Christ, he is a new creation; the old has gone, the new has come! 2 Corinthians 5:17

And we know that in all things God works for the good of those who love him, who have been called according to his purpose. Romans 8:28

Do you not know? Have you not heard? The Lord is the everlasting God, the Creator of the ends of the earth. He will not grow tired or weary, and his understanding no one can fathom. He gives strength to the weary and increases the power of the weak. Even youths grow tired and weary, and young men stumble and fall; but those who hope in the Lord will renew their strength. They will soar on wings like eagles; they will run and not grow weary, they will walk and not be faint. Isaiah 40:28–31

"Ask and it will be given to you; seek and you will find; knock and the door will be opened to you. For everyone who asks receives; he who seeks finds; and to him who knocks, the door will be opened." Matthew 7:7-8

PRAYER

Step Two: Go around and let everyone who wants to answer this question:

"How can we help you in prayer this week?"

Step Three: Spend some time in prayer, remembering those who shared a prayer request. If you would like to say your prayer in silence, say the word "Amen" when you have finished your prayer so that the next person will know when to start.

God wants us to do **WHAT??**

Do We Want to Continue?

OPEN

GATHERING / 15 Minutes / All Together

Leader: You may want to rearrange the agenda and put the ice-breaker into the Caring Time. Save some time at the close for the group to decide about their future. You will need 30 minutes to discuss the covenant on pages 30–31.

Children's Zoo: How would you describe your experience during this course with this group? Choose one of the animals below that best describes how your experience in this group has affected your life. Then share with the group.

WILD EAGLE: because you have helped to heal my wings, and taught me how to soar again

TOWERING GIRAFFE: because you have helped me hold my head up and stick my neck out, and reach over the fences I have built

PLAYFUL PORPOISE: because you have helped me find a new freedom and a whole new world to play in

COLORFUL PEACOCK: because you have told me that I am beautiful; I've started to believe it, and it's changing my life

SAFARI ELEPHANT: because I have enjoyed this new adventure, and I am not going to forget it ... or this group; I can hardly wait for the next safari

LOVABLE HIPPOPOTAMUS: because you have let me surface and bask in the warm sunshine of God's love

LANKY LEOPARD: because you have helped me look very closely at myself and see some of the spots, and you have told me it's okay to be this way

DANCING BEAR: because you have taught me to dance in the midst of pain, and you have helped me reach out and hug again

ROARING LION: because you have let me get down off my mountain, roll in the grass, and not worry about my mane

ALL-WEATHER DUCK: because you have helped me celebrate life—even in stormy weather—and to sing in the rain

BIBLE STUDY / 30 Minutes / Groups of 4

Leader: Make sure to save enough time at the close for caring and decision making. Is the group planning to continue? If so, save some time to work on your "covenant" (Step Three under Caring Time). So work backward on your time requirements.

STUDY

Introduction: The Bible story is about Peter when he has become the leader in the church. Jesus has been crucified ... risen from the dead ... and ascended into heaven. The Holy Spirit has come to indwell the followers of Jesus. At Pentecost, 3,000 people responded to the preaching of Peter and were brought into the church. The Roman authorities are scared. They capture Peter and throw him in jail.

We pick up on the story with Peter in jail and the followers of Jesus praying somewhere in the city. Listen for the feelings as someone reads the story out loud. Then move quickly into groups of 4 and discuss the questionnaire. Be sure to save the last 30-45 minutes for making important decisions about your group at the close of the meeting.

Bible Story: ***Peter's Miraculous Escape From Prison - Acts 12:1–11***

***12** It was about this time that King Herod arrested some who belonged to the church, intending to persecute them. [2]He had James, the brother of John, put to death with the sword. [3]When he saw that this pleased the Jews, he proceeded to seize Peter also. This happened during the Feast of Unleavened Bread. [4]After arresting him, he put him in prison, handing him over to be guarded by four squads of four soldiers each. Herod intended to bring him out for public trial after the Passover.*

[5]So Peter was kept in prison, but the church was earnestly praying to God for him.

[6]The night before Herod was to bring him to trial, Peter was sleeping between two soldiers, bound with two chains, and sentries stood guard at the entrance. [7]Suddenly an angel of the Lord appeared and a light shone in the cell. He struck Peter on the side and woke him up. "Quick, get up!" he said, and the chains fell off Peter's wrists.

[8]Then the angel said to him, "Put on your clothes and sandals." And Peter did so. "Wrap your cloak around you and follow me," the angel told him. [9]Peter followed him out of the prison, but he had no idea that what the angel was doing was really happening; he thought he was seeing a vision. [10]They passed the first and second guards and came to the iron gate leading to the city. It opened for them by itself, and they went through it. When they had walked the length of one street, suddenly the angel left him.

[11]Then Peter came to himself and said, "Now I know without a doubt that the Lord sent his angel and rescued me from Herod's clutches and from everything the Jewish people were anticipating."

Looking Into the Story. The following two-part questionnaire is designed for easy sharing—with multiple-choice options to choose from. Ask one person to answer question #1 and explain why. The next person takes question #2, etc. There are no right or wrong answers, so feel free to share.

1. If one of the people in your group was put to death and another was thrown in jail, what would that do to your group?
- ❑ We would stand up for our faith.
- ❑ It would make us closer.
- ❑ It would cause us to really pray.
- ❑ We would go into hiding.
- ❑ We would give up our faith.
- ❑ I don't know what we would do.

2. Why do you suppose Herod wanted to kill Peter?
- ❑ Peter was a threat to his authority.
- ❑ Peter wouldn't stop preaching.
- ❑ Herod hated Christians.
- ❑ Herod wanted to stay on the good side of the Jewish leaders.

3. How do you think Peter felt as he followed the angel out of prison?
- ❑ wondered what's going on
- ❑ afraid he'd be caught
- ❑ anxious to get out
- ❑ expected a miracle

4. How do you think the guards felt when they found Peter gone?
- ❑ worried for their jobs
- ❑ afraid for their lives
- ❑ ready to follow him
- ❑ angry at Peter for leaving
- ❑ other:______________________

My Own Story: In this step, go around on question #1 and ask everyone to share their answer. Then, go around again on question #2, etc. Remember to save the last 30 to 45 minutes for the Caring Time.

1. Quite frankly, where do you find yourself in prison right now?
   - ❑ in my family relationships
   - ❑ to a craving that holds me captive
   - ❑ to a physical limitation that holds me back
   - ❑ to feelings of low self-worth
   - ❑ other:________________________

2. What would most help you to find freedom from this?
   - ❑ an angel rescuing me
   - ❑ some friends praying for me, and really believing it will happen
   - ❑ confidence in God's ability to help me
   - ❑ my own desire to change
   - ❑ So who wants to change—a prison is a secure place!

3. If an angel from God could enter into your space and touch you on the shoulder, what would he say to you?
   - ❑ "Hurry! Get up!"
   - ❑ "Quit making excuses!"
   - ❑ "There is a group of Christians praying for you."
   - ❑ "I need you to get back into the game."
   - ❑ "Time to go."

4. If this group could assist the angel in your recovery, what could they do?
   - ❑ leave me alone
   - ❑ pray for me
   - ❑ call me every now and then
   - ❑ hold me accountable
   - ❑ help me deal with the relationship that binds me
   - ❑ other:______________________________________

CARING TIME / 45 Minutes / All Together

Leader: This is decision time. The four Steps are designed to help you evaluate your group experience and decide about the future.

EVALUATION

Step One: Take a few minutes to look back over your experience and reflect. Go around on each point and finish the sentences.

1. As I see it, our purpose and goal as a group was to ...

2. We achieved our goal(s):
   - ❑ completely
   - ❑ almost completely
   - ❑ somewhat
   - ❑ We blew it.

3. The high point in this course for me up to now has been:
   - ❑ the Scripture exercises
   - ❑ the sharing
   - ❑ praying together
   - ❑ belonging to a real community of love where you can be honest
   - ❑ bonding together
   - ❑ other:________________________

4. One of the most significant things I learned was ...

5. In my opinion our group functioned:
   - ❑ Smoothly, and we grew.
   - ❑ Pretty well, but we didn't grow.
   - ❑ It was tough, but we grew.
   - ❑ It was tough, and we did not grow.

6. The thing I appreciated most about the group as a whole is ...

Step Two: Continuation. Do you want to continue your group? If so, what do you need to improve? Finish the sentence:

"If I were to suggest one thing we could work on as a group, it would be ..."

MAKE A COVENANT

Step Three: A covenant is a promise made to each other in the presence of God. Its purpose is to indicate our intention to make ourselves available to one another for the fulfillment of the purposes we share in common. In a spirit of prayer, work your way through the following sentences, trying to reach an agreement on each statement pertaining to your ongoing life together. Write out your covenant like a contract, stating your purpose, goals, and the ground rules for your group. Then ask everyone to sign.

1. The purpose of our group will be ... (finish the sentence)

2. Our goals will be ...

3. We will meet for _______ weeks, after which we will decide if we wish to continue as a group.

4. We will meet from ____________________ to __________________ and we will strive to start on time and end on time.

5. We will meet at ________________________________ (place) or we will rotate from house to house.

6. We will agree to the following ground rules for our group (check):

- ❑ PRIORITY: While we are in the group, we will give the group meetings priority.
- ❑ PARTICIPATION: Everyone is given the right to their own opinion, and "dumb questions" are encouraged and respected.
- ❑ CONFIDENTIALITY: Anything that is said in the meeting is never repeated outside the meeting.
- ❑ EMPTY CHAIR: The group stays open to new people at every meeting, as long as they understand the ground rules.
- ❑ SUPPORT: Permission is given to call upon each other in time of need—even in the middle of the night.
- ❑ ACCOUNTABILITY: We agree to let the members of the group hold us accountable to the commitments which each of us make in whatever loving ways we decide upon.

GROUP MATERIALS

Step Four: If you decide to continue as a group for a few more weeks, what are you going to use for study and discipline? Look over the LIFECYCLE OF A GROUP inside the back cover and choose one of the 201 or 301 courses. In the 201 courses, you have two tracks: Option 1 is like this course; Option 2 is deeper Bible study, and you can switch back and forth. 301 Courses are for deeper Bible study with study notes.

For more information about small group resources and possible directions, please contact your small group coordinator or SERENDIPITY at 1-800-525-9563.

SERENDIPITY
COVENANT GROUP CURRICULUM

101

201

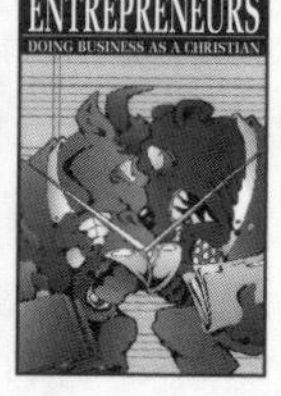

301

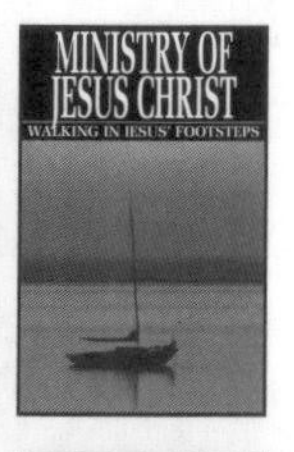